LUDWIG VAN BEETHOVEN

QUARTET

for 2 Violins, Viola and Violoncello
A major/A-Dur/La majeur
Op. 18/5

Edited by/Herausgegeben von
Wilhelm Altmann

T0081297

Ernst Eulenburg Ltd

London · Mainz · New York · Paris · Tokyo · Zürich

BEETHOVEN, 6 STRING QUARTETS, OP. 18

The original hand-written. copies of Beethoven's first six quartets have disappeared if they are not actually lost. After repeated modification and rearrangement, they appeared as op. 18 in two instalments, at the end of June and in October 1801 under the following title: „Six Quatuors pour deux Violons, Alto et Violoncelle, composés et dédiés à Son Altesse Monseigneur le Prince Regnant de Lobkowitz par Louis van Beethoven. Œuvre 18. 1er Livraison à Vienne chez T. Mollo et Comp. (Edition No. 159*). The date of their composition cannot be ascertained for certainty, but it is probably between the years 1798 and 1800, as Gustave Nottebohm has shown from the sketch books. The order of the works chosen by Beethoven at the time of publication was not the original one. At first the D major quartet (No. 3) preceded the one in F major (No. 1), the original form of which, completed on June 25th 1799 and bearing the title of "Quartetto II" was sent by Beethoven to his friend Karl Ferdinand Amenda, with the following letter: "Dear Amenda, Accept this Quartet, as a little remembrance of our friendship. Every time you play it, recall the old days and remember how good to you and always will be was your true and faithful friend Ludwig van Beethoven." It seems to me of great importance that Beethoven on June 1st 1801** , that is to say, shortly before the appearance of the first instalment of his op. 18, should have written to his friend as follows: "Do not part with your quartet, as I have altered it completely, having just mastered the art of quartet writing, as you will see when you receive them." Amenda complied with the composer's wish, and the work remained in his family. In 1904, the possessor of the quartet, Frau Pastor Anna Kawall née Amenda, allowed Dr. Karl Waack in Riga to publish the development section of the first movement in Vol. 10 of the fortnightly "Die Musik". A comparison between the two shows undoubtedly that the revised form is preferable. Amenda also relates that, in the splendid D minor Adagio, Beethoven intended to depict the parting of two lovers, particularly the scene by the vault in Shakespeare's "Romeo and Juliet".

A quartet in C minor was originally intended to be the third; two themes sketched out for this work, were however not used for the later C minor quartet, published as No. 4, but were laid aside in favour of No. 2 in G major, the Finale of which, as well as the Finale of the B flat major quartet (No. 6) and the third and fourth movements of the F major (No. 1) are drafted in one of the sketch books for the years 1799 and 1800.

---

* 169 for the 2nd instalment. I have not seen this original edition, but a later reprint by the same firm (No. 1111 and 1101) which is in the musical collection of the State Library in Berlin.

** This letter bears no year date. Kalischer believes it to be 1800, but I think 1801 is more correct, as Beethoven would hardly have written the words "as you will see when you receive them" if the quartets had not been already published.

The main work on the G major quartet was certainly done in 1799 however, together with the work on the Septet, and the A major quartet, published as No. 5, in which the theme of the Variations was different. In general plan the A major quartet betrays the influence of the quartet by Mozart in the same key.

Sketches for the 4th quartet in C minor have not been preserved. In the new edition of the 2nd volume of Thayer's Beethoven, Hugo Riemann is inclined to regard it as an older work of the Bonn period, which opinion has the approval of Cannabich and Karl Stamitz of Mannheim. He points out in an interesting manner that the first movement is the-matically closely related to, if not identical with, Beethoven's yet unpublished "Duett für zwei obligate Augengläser" or for Viola or Violoncello, which he considers the younger work.

The question of the 5th quartet in A major and the 6th in B flat major was of a different character; it seems that a portion of the Variations of the A major quartet was planned out as early as 1794/5.

The metronome marks now added to our edition were supplied by Beethoven subsequently (see Nottebohm, New Beethoviana 520).

Alterations

1. In the third Variation of Movement III (Andante cantabile) there occurs in the last bar of the first period, a mistake in the Viola part, which until now has been copied into all the published Editions; only the first time, before the repeat, does the upbeat (quaver) occur as an opening to the melodic phrase:

whilst the phrase of the second part:

has no upbeat, which is clearly perceivable in the Violoncello part, and also by the changed form in the first part; (E). Röntgen ought therefore not to have added a fourth quaver (upbeat) into the last bar of the second period before the repeat.

2. In bar 96 of the last movement, there appears in the Viola part, the note of A, tied over from the bar before to the note of C♯. Of course the note must remain A whether it be found a misprint, or after a critical survey. (Dugge) in Heckel (Mannheim, and consequently also in the General-Edition of Breitkopf & Härtel, but not in the Holle-Liszt, and also not in the Joachim-Moser Edition.)

3. In bar 280 there occurs a misprint in the 2nd Edition of Mollo's* and in consequence also in the Breitkopf Edition

the following is preferable:

and is also adopted in the Joachim-Moser Edition by Dugge.

Wilh. Altmann

* Also occurring by Heckel (Mannheim), Holle-Liszt, and Litolff.

BEETHOVEN, 6 STREICHQUARTETTE, OP. 18.

Die Originalhandschriften der ersten sechs Quartette Beethovens, die nach längeren Versuchen und mehrfachen Umarbeitungen als op. 18 in zwei Lieferungen Ende Juni bzw. im Oktober 1801 unter dem Titel: Six Quatuors pour deux Violons, Alto et Violoncelle, composés et dédiés à Son Altesse Monseigneur le Prince Regnant de Lobkowitz && par Louis van Beethoven. Œuvre 18. 1er Livraison à Vienne chez T. Mollo et Comp. (Verlags-No. 159*) in Stimmen erschienen sind, sind verschollen, wenn nicht verloren. Mit Sicherheit läßt sich auch ihre Entstehungszeit nicht angeben; die Hauptarbeit daran dürfte in die Jahre 1798—1800 fallen, wie Nottebohm aus den Skizzenbüchern nachgewiesen hat. Die von Beethoven bei der Drucklegung gewählte Reihenfolge war nicht die ursprüngliche. Zuerst entstand das D-dur-Quartett (No. 3), darauf das in F-dur (No. 1). Dessen ursprüngliche Fassung, die am 25. Juni 1799 vollendet war und ausdrücklich die Bezeichnung „Quartetto II" trägt, schenkte Beethoven seinem Freunde Karl Ferdinand Amenda mit folgendem Briefe: „Lieber Amenda! Nimm dieses Quartett als ein kleines Denkmal unserer Freundschaft. So oft Du Dir es vorspielst, erinnere Dich unserer durchlebten Tage, wie innig gut Dir war und immer sein wird Dein wahrer und warmer Freund Ludwig van Beethoven." Sehr wichtig erscheint mir, daß Beethoven am 1. Juni 1801**), also kurz vor dem Erscheinen der ersten Lieferung seines op. 18 dem Freunde geschrieben hat: „Dein Quartett gib ja nicht weiter, weil ich erst jetzt recht Quartetten zu schreiben weiß, was Du schon sehen wirst, wenn Du sie erhalten wirst." Amenda hat auch diesen Wunsch des Tonsetzers erfüllt; das Quartett ist in seiner Familie geblieben; 1904 erlaubte die damalige Besitzerin Frau Pastor Anna Kawall geb. Amenda in Riga dem Dr. Karl Waack, den Durchführungsteil des ersten Satzes daraus im 10. Bande der Halbmonatsschrift „Die Musik" zu veröffentlichen. Die Handschrift ist aber später in den Besitz des Vereins Beethovenhaus in Bonn übergegangen und 1922 von Dr. Hans Josef Wedig mit eingehenden Untersuchungen veröffentlicht worden, jedoch ohne Drucklegung der Stimmen. Unstreitig ergibt ein Vergleich, daß die neuere Fassung den Vorzug verdient. Amenda hat übrigens auch erzählt, daß Beethoven in dem herrlichen D-moll-Adagio den Abschied zweier Liebenden habe schildern wollen und speziell dabei die Szene im Grabgewölbe aus Shakespeares „Romeo und Julia" im Auge gehabt habe.

Als drittes Quartett war ursprünglich eins in c-moll in Aussicht genommen; zwei skizzierte Themen dazu haben aber in dem später als No. 4 veröffentlichten

---

*) bzw. 169 für die 2. Lieferung. Diese Originalausgabe hat mir nicht vorgelegen, wohl aber ein späterer Druck desselben Verlags (No. 1111, bzw. 1101), den die Musiksammlung der Staatl. Bibliothek zu Berlin besitzt.

**) Dieser Brief trägt keine Jahreszahl. Kalischer glaubt ihn ins Jahr 1800 setzen zu müssen; ich glaube aber, daß 1801 richtiger ist, weil Beethoven die Worte „was Du schon sehen wirst, wenn Du sie erhalten wirst" kaum geschrieben hätte, wenn die Quartette nicht schon im Druck gewesen wären.

C-moll-Quartett keine Verwendung gefunden und wurden zugunsten des Quartetts in G-dur (No. 2) beiseite gelegt; dessen Finale, sowie das Finale des B-dur-Quartetts (No. 6) und der dritte und vierte Satz des F-dur (No. 1) finden sich skizziert in einem in den Jahren 1799 und 1800 benutzten Skizzenbuch. Die Hauptarbeit an dem G-dur-Quartett fällt aber sicherlich in das Jahr 1799 zusammen mit Arbeiten an dem Septett und dem als No. 5 veröffentlichten A-dur-Quartett, in dem damals das Thema der Variationen noch anders lautete. In der ganzen Anlage zeigt sich übrigens dieses A-dur-Quartett von dem in gleicher Tonart stehenden Mozartschen beeinflußt. Den Variationen-Satz desselben hat sich Beethoven selbst in Partitur gesetzt.

Skizzen zu dem 4. Quartett in c-moll sind nicht erhalten. Hugo Riemann (Neubearbeitung des 2. Bandes von Thayers Beethoven) ist geneigt, es für eine ältere Arbeit (noch aus der Bonner Zeit) zu

halten und findet Anklänge an die Mannheimer Cannabich und Karl Stamitz. Mir scheint er dieses C-moll-Quartett erheblich zu unterschätzen. Sehr interessant ist sein Nachweis, daß der erste Satz thematisch sehr nahe verwandt, ja fast gleichlautend mit Beethovens damals noch unveröffentlichtem, erst 1912 durch Fritz Stein herausgekommenen „Duett für zwei obligate Augengläser" oder vielmehr für Viola und Violoncell ist, das er für jünger hält.

Vom 5. Quartett in A-dur, ebenso vom 6. in B-dur war schon in anderem Zusammenhang die Rede; nachzutragen ist noch, daß ein Stück der Variationen des A-dur-Quartetts schon 1794/5 skizziert zu sein scheint.

Die unserer Ausgabe jetzt hinzugefügte Metronomisierung hat Beethoven nachträglich festgestellt (vgl. Nottebohm, Neue Beethoviana 520).

Varianten

1. In der dritten Variation des III. Satzes (Andante cantabile) ist der Schlußtakt der ersten Periode in allen Ausgaben der Viola bisher falsch gedruckt; nur beim ersten Mal gehört das letzte Achtel als Auftakt zu der melodischen Phrase

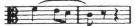

während die Phrase des zweiten Teils

keinen Auftakt hat, was ganz deutlich aus der Violoncellstimme und auch aus der abgeänderten Form im ersten Teile hervorgeht; Röntgen durfte daher in dem letzten Takt der zweiten Periode vor der Wiederholung nicht ein viertes Achtel ergänzen.

2. Im Schlußsatz findet sich im Takt 96 im andern bei Heckel, Mannheim, und natürlich infolgedessen auch in der kritischen Gesamtausgabe von B. & H. (nicht bei Holle-

Liszt, nicht bei Joachim-Moser) in der Violastimme das vom vorhergehenden Takte gebundene a als c. — Natürlich muß es, gleichviel ob Stichfehler oder Ergebnis einer „kritischen" Untersuchung, auf jeden Fall a heißen. (Dugge.)

3. Im Takt 280 ist in der Violastimme dem mit einem Stichfehler der 2. Mollo'schen Ausgabe (der auch Heckel [Mannheim], Holle-Liszt und Litolff folgen) übereinstimmenden kritischen Resultat der Breitkopf & Härtelschen Ausgabe

die Lesart

vorzuziehen, die auch Joachim-Moser von Dugge adoptiert haben.

Wilh. Altmann

Quartet

L. van Beethoven, Op. 18 Nº 5
1770 - 1827

I

E. E. 1120   Ernst Eulenburg Ltd

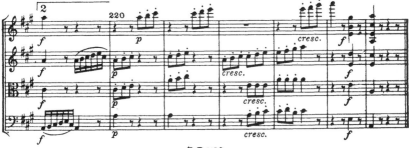

Menuetto ♩.=76

II

Andante cantabile ♪= 100

III

Var. 1

Var. 2

E. E. 1120

Var. 3

Var. 4.

Var. 5.

E.E.1120

IV

26

E. E. 1120

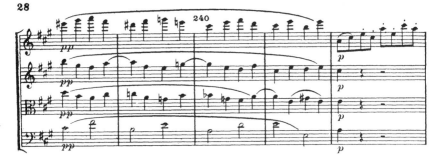

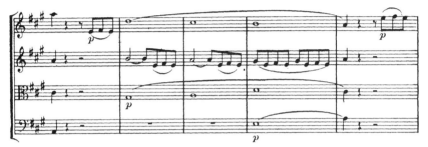

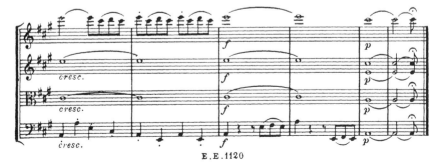